Understanding
STRESS

Professor Greg Wilkinson

Published by Family Doctor Publications Limited
in association with the British Medical Association

IMPORTANT NOTICE

This book is intended not as a substitute for personal medical advice but as a supplement to that advice for the patient who wishes to understand more about his/her condition.

Before taking any form of treatment YOU SHOULD ALWAYS CONSULT YOUR MEDICAL PRACTITIONER.

In particular (without limit) you should note that advances in medical science occur rapidly and some of the information about drugs and treatment contained in this booklet may very soon be out of date.

Family Doctor Publications, PO Box 4664, Poole, Dorset BH15 1NN

Medical Editor: Dr Tony Smith
Consultant Editor: Chris McLaughlin
Cover Artist: Dave Eastbury
Cartoonist: Dave Eastbury
Design: MPG Design, Blandford Forum, Dorset
Printing: Reflex Litho, Thetford, using acid-free paper

ISBN: 1 898205 91 4

Contents

Coping with stress

What causes stress? Anything that makes you tense, angry, frustrated or unhappy. It may be thinking about next week's driving test or a visit from a difficult relative; the choices you have to make when moving house or getting married; the seemingly unrelenting pressures of work; or the unavoidable burden of coping with a death in the family.

Factors that stress some people give others excitement. Racing drivers and mountaineers seem to thrive on physical challenges. Some people enjoy the excitement of going to sea in bad weather and join the lifeboat crew. Others choose to work on high buildings and rooftops. So, one person's stress may be another person's pleasure.

In fact, a certain amount of stress is good for us. When we have to face up to a challenge or we are made to get on with some job we don't want to do, we often find that we can achieve the targets we have been set. We then feel a lot better having done it. Facing challenges and overcoming them stops us from getting bored. In fact, many people deliberately create mild stress in their lives to overcome periods of dull routine.

Too much stress, however, affects our health and well-being, and may interfere with our jobs and our social lives. Repeated, continuing, severe stress has a weakening and demoralising effect, which may make it more difficult to do anything about the factors that are causing the stress.

Just how we respond to pressure is determined by our dealing with the unexpected. We learn to make adjustments in attitude, and the way we behave, in order to understand and to cope. Usually this is fairly straightforward and we are hardly aware that we are 'coping with stress'.

When events of major importance take place, however, such as marriage, birth or the death of someone close, our reactions and

characters, and by our personal disabilities or illnesses. These dictate how we react to difficulties with relationships, both at home and at work, and to practical problems over money, work and housing.

A QUESTION OF ADJUSTMENT

As we grow and mature we become better at knowing what to expect in our everyday life, and what to do about the things that upset us. We become better at the way we cope are more obvious to us.

In order to live successfully with stress, we need to spend some time considering the sources of stress in our lives and whether our physical and emotional responses to these are sensible and useful, or are preventing us from coping and taking control.

Although studies show that the ability to cope is partly inborn, it is also a question of training, upbringing and practice.

A survey by the Health and Safety Executive has shown that half a million Britons suffer illnesses related to stress at work, and this is probably an underestimate.

OVERCOMING STRESS

There is every reason to be optimistic that you will be able to overcome the stress in your life. There are several simple and effective methods that can be used to reduce and overcome stress, and, in most cases, these self-help solutions are very successful.

Although almost everyone is under some form of stress, only a few ever respond by developing a physical or emotional illness that requires specialist help.

KEY POINTS

✓ Stress is caused by anything that makes you tense, angry, frustrated or unhappy

✓ One person's stress may be someone else's enjoyment

✓ A certain level of stress is good for us

✓ Too much stress affects our health and well-being

✓ There is every reason to be optimistic that you will be able to overcome the stress in your life

Balancing coping and stress

I have already said that stress can be both a good thing – a motivator – and a bad thing. Furthermore, what is stressful may not only vary from one person to another, but can change for one individual from year to year.

This is because the way that stress affects us depends on a balance between the demand made by the event(s) causing the stress and our ability to cope (which can vary considerably). Too large an imbalance between demand and ability to cope may result in the sort of stress that is not good for us.

Looked at in a slightly different way, the overall level of stress depends on a complicated balance that takes account of the stressful event, our response to this in terms of physical effects, emotions and

THE LEVEL OF STRESS

| Stress level = | Potentially stressful event(s) | + | Our response to the event(s) (physical, emotional or behavioural) | + | Significance of the event(s) to us (happy, sad, worried or indifferent) |

outward behaviour, and how significant the event is to us (is it something that makes us very happy, deeply sad or is it not too important?).

For example, if John Smith, with a large mortgage, a wife, three children and a job that he enjoys and is important to him, is made redundant, he is put under a great deal of stress. The event is of major significance to him, and he may suffer physical symptoms (inability to sleep, eat or relax), and emotional reactions (bursts of anger and irritation) which affect his outward behaviour.

Jill Brown, on the other hand, is 23, highly qualified, with no responsibilities and a job that she finds boring. If she is made redundant, she may not be shattered. Instead, she may feel that the event has forced her to make a long overdue change, and she may be relieved and relax, feeling better than she has done in ages. In this case, stress has a positive side and is needed to introduce a necessary element of change in her life.

We can see from this that similar stress events may bring out an entirely different response in different people.

KEY POINTS

✓ The way stress affects us depends on a balance between the demands made and our ability to cope

✓ Physical symptoms of stress may sometimes result from an individual's inability to deal with it

We would all become extremely bored if nothing ever happened in our lives. However, any major change needs to be balanced with our ability to cope with that particular change at the time in question.

Too much change, too quickly, can be a major cause of stress. The demands are far too much for our ability to cope. An indication of how much stress various typical life events and social changes may cause is given in the table on page 7.

In general, the greater the number of these events that happen to us in a given time, such as a year, and the higher their combined rating, the more likely we are to suffer a stress response, either emotional or physical. Moreover, the severity of the stress response is usually related to the significance of the events and changes.

Remember that stress can be triggered off by events that are thought of as pleasant, such as getting married, winning money or having a baby, as well as by unpleasant events such as losing a job, having an accident or the illness of someone in the family.

LIFE EVENTS AND STRESS

Events	Stress rating
Death of husband or wife Divorce or marital separation Jail term Death of close family member Personal injury or illness Marriage Loss of job Moving house	Very high
Marital reconciliation Retirement Serious illness of family member Pregnancy Sex difficulties New child Change of job Money problems Death of close friend	High
Family arguments Big mortgage or loan Legal action over debt Change in responsibilities at work Son or daughter leaving home Trouble with in-laws Outstanding personal achievement Wife begins or stops work Start or finish of school Change in living conditions Revision of personal habits Trouble with boss	Moderate
Change in work hours or conditions Change in schools Change in recreation Change in church activities Change in social activities Small mortgage or loan Change in sleeping habits Change in contact with family Change in eating habits Holidays Christmas Minor violations of the law	Low

Adapted from Holmes and Rahe.

- Unpredictable
- Unfamiliar
- Major
- Intense
- Unavoidable
- Inevitable.

Do be careful, however, not to take the contents of the table on page 7 too literally. It is common for people who feel stressed to search for the reason in past events, but some can be the result, rather than the cause, of the stress.

A feeling of not being able to cope with new duties or responsibilities, for example, may be the result of unrecognised stress rather than the stress being the result of a failure to cope with the situation.

So sources of stress lie mainly in these events in our lives and in our

LIFE EVENTS

When evaluating the impact of life events and social changes as a cause of stress, we also need to take into account the fact that they tend to be particularly stressful when they are:

WHAT FACTORS AFFECT YOU?

To help discover the source of your stress, ask yourself whether there are any social, physical or emotional factors that are affecting you:

- How many tea/coffee/caffeinated drinks are you having?
- How much are you smoking?
- How much alcohol are you drinking?
- Are you taking enough exercise?
- Could you be ill?
- Is there some new element in your life?
- Has there been any change in your general circumstances?
- Have long-standing problems recently become worse?
- Is someone close to you facing difficulties that affect you?

physical and emotional responses to such events. The cause may be obvious to us, in which case the way we need to react may be straightforward and clear cut, and depend on us making practical or emotional adjustments. In these circumstances, it may be easy to see where we should ask for help.

Often, though, the source of stress is not quite so obvious and it may need some careful thought or talking through with others to bring it out in the open. Again, unrecognised illness may affect our ability to cope, or there may be difficulties with relationships that we are not prepared to face.

Sometimes, however, we may never find an answer and very occasionally stress does come 'out of the blue'.

LIFE PHASES

You may get a clue about stress levels from considering the phase of life you are in. In the late teens, many major decisions have to be made for the first time. In mid-life, responsibilities are often heaviest and most dramatic. In old age, there may be illness, deaths in the family and money problems to cope with on your own.

You should also consider the phases of life that those close to you are in. Crying babies, bedtime blues, little monsters, know-it-alls, getting to school, teenage rebels – no parent gets it right every time. Even family mealtimes can be the most stressful occasions in everyday life.

CONFLICTS IN YOUR LIFE

Ask yourself whether there is anything that you would like to sort out. For example:

- Do you have continual disagreements about someone or about something?
- Is some situation leaving you with a feeling that you are not good enough, or that it is all your fault?
- Are you taking, or being made to take, a new or unaccustomed role – or are you perhaps carrying, or being asked to carry, too much responsibility?
- Do you have unspoken fears or frustrations about your life?

Often stress is the result of a build-up of related and unrelated factors of these kinds. If you settle down quietly and list the stresses in your life, you may be surprised – and relieved – to discover some of the stresses are ones that you can eliminate.

THE WARNING SIGNS OF STRESS

The warning signs that stress may be affecting your health vary considerably from person to person. Most of us, however, have our own usual stress response or 'fingerprint'.

This might be headaches in one person, or an outbreak of eczema or diarrhoea in another. Usually the first signs of stress are changes in our emotional life or behaviour, and at times the differences can become more noticeable to others than they are to us.

EMOTIONAL REACTIONS

The most important changes to watch out for are increases in tension, irritability and moodiness. Small irritations may seem unbearable if they come on top of stress, and can cause a major outburst or upset. For example, the fact that the children want to play a board game when you have just come home from work, and you simply want to sit down and relax, may make you feel that you want to put them up for adoption; or you may find that you have an overwhelming desire to perpetrate grievous bodily harm on your car when it refuses to start; and when the toaster will not pop up your slice of toast you have to be held back from attacking it with the bread knife.

There may also be changes in appetite or weight: some people lose interest in food, whereas others have a constant desire to eat. Your ability to cope at home and at work may become extremely variable: you may find you can't quite get round to paying the household bills, and are spurred into action only when the phone has been disconnected; and your brain seems to have moved into reverse gear at work so that the 'in tray' gets bigger and bigger. You smoke or drink (or both) more, which does, however, help fill in the time in the evening as you seem to have difficulty in sleeping.

The box on page 12 gives some examples of different emotional reactions to stress. If you notice some of these signs or other people point them out to you, take notice; unless you take steps to protect yourself, you are at risk of experiencing increasing stress. You may not recognise all the signs at first, however, or you may have overlooked or ignored some for a variety of reasons. You may also have to resist a tendency to regard the reactions as definite evidence of serious physical illness rather than a response to stress.

EMOTIONAL REACTIONS TO STRESS

- Feeling under pressure
- Feeling tense and unable to relax
- Feeling mentally drained

- Being constantly frightened
- Increasing irritability and complaining
- Feeling of conflict
- Frustration and aggression
- Restlessness, increasing inability to concentrate, or to complete tasks quickly
- Increased tearfulness
- Become more fussy, gloomy or suspicious
- Being unable to take decisions
- Impulses to run and hide
- Fears of imminent fainting, collapse or death
- Fears of social embarrassment or failure
- Lacking in ability to feel pleasure or enjoyment

PHYSICAL REACTIONS

Physical reactions to strong emotions were designed to save us in the days when we led the simple, dangerous life of the caveman. To Stone Age man these bodily responses meant fight or flight and prepared him for action; millions of years later they still do – which is very useful if a woolly mammoth is on the rampage, but not a great deal of help

when we have just missed the last train or dropped the car keys down a drain in the road! What happens to our body is that our pulse and blood pressure increase, we breathe more rapidly and our ears, eyes and nose become more alert. These changes are the result of the action of stress hormones released into the blood circulation in response to the event.

When the stress response goes on for a long time, or occurs frequently and at the wrong time, it may lead to a wide range of unpleasant feelings. The number and nature of physical feelings differ greatly between people, but the most common are listed in the box on page 14. The most effective techniques for dealing with physical reactions to stress are controlled deep breathing and relaxation. These are discussed on pages 33–6. It is important to be relaxed regularly throughout the day and not only when you are 'relaxing'.

Try to start noticing bodily sensations and, whenever you feel physical reactions to stress, try to relax your muscles; for example, drop your shoulders, and relax your facial and tummy muscles. If you can, stop what you are doing and rest, spend time quietly calming down, and practise distracting yourself, deep breathing and relaxing your muscles. Start by taking a deep breath and slowing down your breathing. Take a deep breath, hold it in while you count up to three ('one hundred and one, one hundred and two, one hundred and three') and then slowly breathe out.

Repeat this exercise and continue slow, relaxed breathing at around 10 breaths per minute. If you feel comfortable, you can increase to a 'six-second breath', counting one hundred and one through to one hundred and six. (Fast shallow breathing can increase

PHYSICAL REACTIONS TO STRESS

- Muscle tension
- Rapid, uneven or pounding heartbeat
- Fast, shallow breathing
- Sweating
- Dilated pupils
- Over-alertness
- Change in appetite
- Muscle weakness or trembling
- A sick feeling in the stomach
- Sleep problems
- Jumpiness
- Headaches
- Weakness of the limbs
- Indigestion
- Frequent urge to pass urine
- Chest discomfort
- Odd aches, pains or twitches
- Constipation or diarrhoea
- Tiredness and weakness
- Worsening of long-standing discomforts or pain
- Constant restlessness and fidgeting
- Backache
- 'Pins and needles' in hands or feet
- Dry mouth or throat
- 'Butterflies' in the stomach

physical reactions to stress.) Then slowly go back to what you were doing or carry on to where you were going – continue to breathe slowly and deeply, distracting yourself, and thinking constructively and positively about how you handled the situation and how you will deal with it should it recur.

BEHAVIOURAL REACTIONS

The behaviour of people under stress can change quite considerably. Often they hate to be alone and make efforts to seek out support from family and friends. Some may become withdrawn and indifferent. They seem to have lost interest in others and even start to turn down invitations because everything feels as if it will cause too much trouble.

They continually seek reassurance and can become indecisive – a trip to the supermarket for a packet of tea bags seems to require as much thought and preparation as the ascent of Everest. They change their minds a lot and they may speak fondly of someone one moment and find them completely useless the next. They may be tearful, difficult and complaining, and often expect others to be impossibly understanding of them.

There may be a change in sexual habits (a loss of interest, an increase in casual sex or altered sexual preference), and the previously mild-mannered may become verbally or physically aggressive.

A person who used to be fairly relaxed may become rigid and obsessive, repeatedly checking locks and switches, for example, or cleaning the oven at three in the morning when previously it was done once a year.

Actions of this sort may be due to an effort to bring some order and certainty to the sense of confusion which they feel is surrounding them. Often the person under stress denies these behavioural changes but they are usually very obvious to other people.

Ask friends whether they have noticed any changes in your behaviour, but don't be cross with them for telling the truth – remember that denying the obvious can be a sign of stress!

KEY POINTS

✓ Too much change too quickly can be a cause of stress

✓ Stress can be caused by pleasant and unpleasant events

✓ The cause of stress may not always be apparent

✓ Usually stress is a result of build-up of related and unrelated events

✓ Often your stress is more apparent to others than to yourself

✓ Reactions to stress can be emotional, physical and behavioural

Tackling the problem

The difficult thing about stress is recognising it; doing something about it is relatively easy. Once you have recognised that you are suffering a stress response, you should be able to identify and tackle any underlying causes, not just the symptoms. And you can ask someone you trust and respect to help.

KEEPING A RECORD

First of all list all your signs of stress, noting how severe they are and for how long they have lasted. Next, list all the possible causes you can think of and sort them into categories.

Remember that a series of minor irritations may be more distressing than the major problems of life.

Having written down all the possible causes of your stress, you can sort them into those that have a practical solution, those that will get better anyway, given time, and those that you can do nothing to change. You should try to let go of those that fall into the second and third groups – what you cannot change try to stop worrying about. Your teenage daughter may give up her attempts to be a model and go back to college, or she may be so successful she becomes a million-airess. The drilling outside may be a

SAMPLE STRESS DIARY

Stress sign	Severity (out of 10)	How long it lasted	Catego
Sleeplessness	I often lie awake for hours (9/10)	The last six weeks	Family and friends
Under pressure	I dread going to work in the morning (7/10)	At least three months	
Racing heart	Sometimes I feel faint (5/10)	The last two weeks	
6 weeks later Sleeplessness	Difficulty sleeping (5/10)	Three nights last week	Work
Under pressure	Feel better about going into work if I stop for breakfast in a nearby café (3/10)		
Racing heart	Not too bad last week (1/10)		
12 weeks later Sleeplessness	Better since altered bedtime routine and exercising regularly (1–2/10)		Leisure interest
Under pressure	Got to consider my next career move – is this the right time? (1/10)		Finance
Racing heart	Better with breathing exercises and relaxation tape (1/10)		Health appeara Home environn

ble cause ess	What type of stress?			Possible solution(s)
	Has a practical solution	Will get better with time	Cannot influence or change	
other has had fall			X	You cannot change what has happened; ensure that the family help her
aughter has ed out of college		X		She knows her own mind and in time you will accept the situation
that I am being ut	X			The solution is in your hands, get involved in: family, clubs, sport, voluntary work, local politics, education
pushing myself ard	X			There are practical steps you can take: structure your time, delegate more, give yourself space to think, prioritise activities, have proper breaks during the day, discuss workload with boss/ colleagues, reorganise tasks to achieve a balance
end deadlines		X		They will pass and so will your stress
nd all my spare watching telly	X			Develop a wider range of interests: arts/crafts, sport, films, concerts, theatre, reading
t card account	X			Stop using it or use it only for essentials
getting old			X	Accept the situation and grow old gracefully
usband is taking a time re-decorating		X		Offer to help, be patient!

distant memory a month from now.

Where there *are* practical solutions (and this applies to most problems) make a list of these and try them out to see if they improve the situation.

You should be prepared for the fact that some of these solutions may upset people. Remember that looking after yourself does not mean being unkind to others, and that you are most useful to yourself and to others if you are functioning well.

Monitoring progress

The next stage is to monitor your stress response by keeping a note or brief diary of the changes in the nature, severity or duration of the signs. After a week, repeat the process to see how you are getting on: if some of the solutions do not seem to be working, try alternatives.

Keep assessing progress until you feel that you have reduced as many of the causes of stress as possible and that you are in control of things. Almost certainly things will have vastly improved over 6 to 12 weeks.

In particular, you need to consider four aspects of persistent unhelpful thoughts:

1 How do they relate to the facts?
2 What are the alternative interpretations?
3 What are the pros and cons of thinking this way?
4 Are you jumping to conclusions or blaming yourself unnecessarily?

ANALYSING YOUR THINKING

Thinking about thinking is not something we usually do and you may find it difficult at first. It is difficult to think of different options when you feel stressed.

CONTROLLING YOUR LIFESTYLE

Too much to do and too much responsibility? To avoid feeling overwhelmed you can divide chores into what you 'must' do, what you 'should' do and what you 'need not' do. The following points may help you to feel more in control of your life:

1   Plan a daily or a weekly timetable of activities. Include something new or different each day.
2   Plan for the future and do not dwell on past mistakes or disappointments.
3   Cut down on smoking, alcohol, caffeinated drinks; exercise regularly; eat proper meals; get enough sleep.
4   Find time for rest and relaxation.
5   Involve your family and friends in helping to change your lifestyle.

CHANGING YOUR THINKING

To change the way that you think, you need to:

- Think about your thinking. Reward your successes and challenge your criticisms.
- Look out for and record unhelpful thoughts that pop into your mind without any effort on your part, that do not fit the facts, that you don't question and that are difficult to switch off. Write down as much as possible to begin with. Fast, effective responses will become easier with practice.
- Learn to recognise unhelpful ways of thinking and substitute more realistic and helpful thoughts. By regular practice this will become easier. Start off by writing your thoughts down until you get the hang of it.
- Resist the temptation to avoid thinking about unhelpful thoughts but beware of making excuses – ignoring the problem will not make it go away.
- Record as many unhelpful thoughts and your responses to them as possible each day. You may need to work out 50–100 responses to unhelpful thoughts before you can do it in your head. Write down as much as possible to begin with. Effective responses will become easier with practice.

1 Write down your hourly timetable. For each activity score 0 to 10 for the pleasure it gives you and 0 to 10 for how well you carry it out. Keep a check on your progress every few days.

2 Make a list of what you need to do.

3 Plan your timetable to:

- Do things that need to be done
- Do things that give you more pleasure
- Do things that you can do well.

4 Concentrate on goals that are achievable all at once or in small steps.

5 Check for unhelpful patterns of thinking, such as: 'I can't cope with this'; 'I've got to get out of this'. How true are these thoughts? Are there other ways of thinking about the situation?

6 Write down the problem(s) and all the possible options for change and then try them out beginning with the most achievable.

RECOGNISE UNHELPFUL THOUGHTS

1 Count up how many unhelpful thoughts you have each day and how much of the time was taken up with these thoughts.

For example, you might feel you have to put up with a shoddy repair job at home because you feel you wouldn't know what to say if you tried to complain. Or that a meeting went badly at work because you are not up to your job. Over several days you may begin to see a pattern emerging.

**If something leads to more unhelpful thoughts
– AVOID IT**

**If something leads to fewer unhelpful thoughts
– DO MORE OF IT**

2 Use unhelpful thoughts as a cue for action. Write them down as they occur in a daily diary.

Just write down what is troubling you and return to it when you feel more at ease. There is no right answer; look for solutions that help you be more positive.

When every movement seems an effort, the best response can be to make yourself do more.

Benefitting from activities

Any activity is positive, because it:

- Makes you feel better. It distracts you, it gives you a sense of control over your life, achievement and pleasure.
- Gives you the strength and stamina to feel less tired
- Helps you become motivated. The more you do the more you want to do.
- Helps you think straight.
- Pleases those around you.

TWENTY QUESTIONS TO HELP YOU DEAL WITH UNHELPFUL THOUGHTS

1 Is it a thought or is it a fact?

2 Jumping to conclusions?

3 What is the alternative?

4 What is the effect on me of thinking this way?

5 What are the advantages and disadvantages?

6 Is there any answer to this? (What is the meaning of life?)

7 Am I thinking in black and white terms?

8 Are the issues really as clear cut as 'always versus never' and 'everything versus nothing'?

9 Is everything wrong because of one event or change?

10 Are my weaknesses over-shadowing my strengths?

11 How appropriate is blame?

12 How much of this is to do with me?

13 How perfect can I be?

14 Have I got double standards?

15 Is there only a down side?

16 Is everything likely to be a disaster?

17 Are things out of proportion?

18 Am I living life the way it is or the way I'd wish it to be?

19 Isn't there anything that can change?

20 What can I do to affect the outcome?

Making an activity schedule

An activity schedule gives you information about what you are doing now and what more you can do in the future. It confirms that you are not 'doing nothing'.

For three days record exactly what you do hour by hour. Give each activity a rating between 0 and 10 for enjoyment (E), pleasure (P), achievement (A) and mastery (M), with 10 being the most rewarding and 0 the least.

E10 means that the activity was highly enjoyable and A10 means there was a high sense of achievement.

Make the ratings at the time of the activity and not in retrospect, and relate them to you as you are now and not how you once were at some perfect time in the past.

Planning activities

What would you like to improve? How can you change things for the better?

Plan each day in advance, including activities that give you enjoyment and a sense of achievement

- Structuring time allows you to feel that you are gaining control and have a sense of purpose.
- A daily or weekly framework provides meaningful structure for living.

- Once the day or the week's activities are planned and structured, they are broken down into a series of manageable units that are less overwhelming.

Making the most of activities

- Be flexible, not a slave to routine.
- Think of alternatives — you can't picnic when it rains.
- Keep to the plan. If you have some 'free time', fill it in with something from a list of pleasurable activities you keep handy.
- Schedule activities by the half hour or hour.
- Concentrate on how much time you are going to spend, not how much you are going to do in the time available. You weed for an hour, not to collect a hundredweight of weeds!
- Work to the schedule. Work steadily to gain results.
- Review the situation. What have you enjoyed achieving?

Getting started

Try combating your problems in the following way:

- Make a list of things you have been putting off, such as getting the car serviced, phoning an awkward relative.

WRITE DOWN DIFFICULTIES YOU SEE AND HOW TO GET ROUND THEM

Difficulties	Alternatives
X I can't cope with having the in-laws to lunch.	✓ If I write down what I need to do it won't be so over-whelming. I can take the things one at a time. I don't have to do them all at once.
X It's too difficult to sort out the muddle at work.	✓ I've done more difficult things than this in the past.
X I don't want to go to an exercise class.	✓ I don't now but I did earlier on. It would be better for me to do it. I'll feel good about it afterwards.
X I don't think I'm up to making a difficult phone call just now.	✓ I won't know until I try. If I wait till I feel like it I'll never do it. I'll feel better when I've done it.
X I won't be able to do everything I've planned because there simply isn't enough time.	✓ No one does all they've planned. Think about what I have done, not what I haven't.
X I can't decide which thing to do first because they're all equally important.	✓ Do the first in alphabetical order. The most important thing is to do something. Once I get started I'll have a clearer idea of what to do next.

- Number tasks in order of priority and try to do those with the highest priority. For example, if your car is making odd noises and hasn't been near a garage for months, that job should be near the top of your list.
- Break the first task into small steps:
  Check your diary to see whether you'll be needing the car for something vital

Find the garage phone number
Ring and book it in.

- When you face a difficult task, rehearse the task in your mind step by step.

Writing it down

Write down difficulties you foresee and how to get round them.

- Stop when you are doing well and you will feel good about what you have achieved and ready to try again.

- When you finish, immediately write down what you have done on your activity schedule and rate it for enjoyment and achievement.
- Concentrate on achievements.

Remember next time

- Go back and look at your priority list again.
- Tackle the next task in the same way.

KEY POINTS

✓ Once you have recognised that you are suffering a stress response, then you should be able to identify and tackle any underlying causes

✓ List your signs of stress

✓ List the probable causes of your stress

✓ Monitor the changes in the nature, severity or duration of the signs of your stress

✓ Look out for unhelpful thoughts and think of new solutions to them

✓ Try your solutions out

✓ Plans and activities are powerful weapons to overcome stress

Defences against stress

We can defend ourselves against stress in our lives by understanding what causes us stress, and by learning how to avoid or adjust and adapt better. The principal defences are within ourselves, and mainly consist of physical and mental fitness – a healthy body and a healthy mind.

PHYSICAL DEFENCES

We can improve our defences by leading a healthy, enjoyable life and by looking after ourselves.

Sleep

First, we should ensure that we get enough sleep and this can be helped by learning how to relax (see table on pages 34–5). Sleep does 'knit up the ravelled sleeve of care'. The amount needed varies from person to person, but it is probably true to say that more is needed during times of stress than when life is running quietly and smoothly. Beware, however, of taking too much sleep – it can make you feel almost as bad as too little. Sleeping problems are very common among those under stress, but do make sure that you do not worry unnecessarily about a few bad nights – you can usually catch up after one good night's sleep.

If you are having difficulty in sleeping, reduce your overall daily consumption of tea, coffee and soft drinks containing caffeine; eat supper early and avoid strong tea or coffee, unless it is decaffeinated, in the afternoon and evening. Try to tire yourself physically by taking some pleasant exercise, for example, a brisk walk or gardening, have a bath and then spend some time switching your mind off before going to bed by reading or watching television or even playing 'patience'. Do not allow yourself to brood over problems; they can wait until the morning! If you can't get to sleep, or wake in the middle of the night and can't get to sleep again, get up, make yourself a drink (preferably with hot milk, and not tea or coffee), have another game of 'patience' or do some mindless chore like sorting your sock drawer out or tidying the tool box, and then go back to bed. Do not lie in bed worrying.

Try not to take sleeping pills unless it's only for one or two nights in order to break the pattern of sleeplessness. They can make you feel fuzzy and dopey in the morning, and can develop into an unwelcome habit which could end up causing even more stress.

Diet

Try to keep to the ideal weight for your height. We should all eat a sensible diet to avoid the health hazards of being overweight, and to reduce or prevent the risks of developing diseases known to be related to diet, such as heart disease, high blood pressure, bowel cancer and late-onset diabetes.

The main principles are to eat far less fat and fatty foods, especially those containing saturated fats and cholesterol; increase dietary fibre by eating more whole-grain cereals, pulses and fresh fruit and vegetables; cut down on sugar and salt. This can be difficult as it goes against all that many of us hold dear, such as the traditional Sunday lunch of roast beef, Yorkshire pudding and roast potatoes! Don't go too quickly in your campaign for diet reform; change a few products at a time and add new foods rather than just cutting out those that you currently eat and are bad for you. If you live for Sunday roast lunch, don't abandon it completely. Just try to cut back on the fatty bits.

WHAT SHOULD YOU WEIGH?

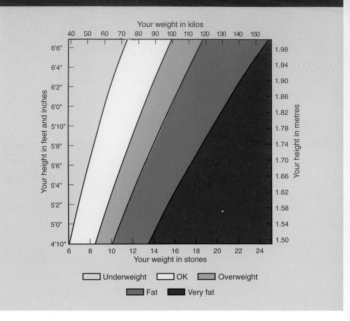

Your weight in kilos

Your height in feet and inches

Your height in metres

Your weight in stones

- ☐ Underweight
- ☐ OK
- ☐ Overweight
- ■ Fat
- ■ Very fat

Changing your diet should not be a torture – it should be fun!

Be careful about what you drink. Too much tea or coffee can be over-stimulating and excessive alcohol is certainly no friend to good health. You should also avoid drinks with a lot of sugar or caffeine.

Exercise

There is only one way to keep the body trim and fit – by exercise. We all need some regular exercise, preferably daily. This might amount to no more than a pleasant, brisk 20-minute walk in the fresh air, but it could well be much more. At the very least, you will be more likely to feel physically and mentally relaxed, be able to get a refreshing sleep and your appetite will be stimulated. The important thing is

HELPING YOURSELF WITH EXERCISE

Whatever you decide to do in the way of exercise, always bear the following points in mind:

- Warm up for two or three minutes before starting by stretching or running on the spot.
- Build up slowly and do not over-extend yourself – always exercise within the limits of comfort (let your breathing be your guide) and, if it hurts, stop.
- If you feel excessively tired, stop and rest – there is always tomorrow.
- When stopping exercise, cool down gradually and slowly to avoid stiffness.
- Exercise sessions three times a week for about 20 minutes, at a pace that keeps you moderately 'puffed' (not gasping for breath), are likely to be best for stimulating both muscles and circulation.

that the exercise chosen should be pleasurable – which for some of us is a problem!

MENTAL DEFENCES

Improving general health and fitness can protect against and lessen the effects of stress. Some events are in themselves stressful, but many of our reactions to these depend on our attitudes, beliefs and values. The mind has a whole series of defence mechanisms, described in the last section of this book, and although these may be helpful in the short term, they may act as a barrier to adapting and coping with stress.

In overcoming stress we often do not have appropriate or enough coping strategies available. We need to learn new skills of self-instruction and self-control.

SELF-INSTRUCTION

When we learn a new skill, such as driving a car, we learn from a combination of observation and instruction. At the beginning, we are usually instructed by someone else; then we repeat the process, giving the instructions to ourselves;

finally, once we have learned the skills, we are able to drive 'automatically' without consciously thinking of what we are doing.

We can apply a similar process of:
- observation
- instruction
- self-instruction
- automatic ability

to our everyday thinking.

For example, suppose we feel stressed about taking examinations or having job interviews. First, using a little imagination before the event, we can pay attention to the way our thoughts tend to work when the stress is imminent. What are the things that we say to ourselves? Perhaps 'Oh, my God, what can I say?'; 'I wish this was all over'; 'I wish I hadn't started this'; 'Two hours still to go'; 'They must think I'm an idiot'; and so on.

Next, we can make a list of positive, practical instructions that would be more useful. Such as 'I had better start writing' rather than 'I'm very nervous'; or 'These are the main points and these are things I want to emphasise' rather than 'I don't know what they're looking for'.

Third, during the event, we instruct ourselves positively with the most useful instructions we have thought of beforehand, instead of wasting time and energy panicking or ruminating on irrelevant thoughts. In time this process becomes 'automatic'.

SELF-CONTROL

Having a sense of control over events lessens their stressful impact. True, there are some things over which we have no control, but there is usually some aspect of a problem that we can change to our advantage, thereby reducing stressful feelings of helplessness.

Self-control methods can be very useful when we wish to alter particular aspects of our behaviour or response to people or events.

First, carefully observe the behaviour in question, for example, always getting angry with Bloggins at work, or being irritable with the family at breakfast time, or regularly missing the bus/train because you leave home with too little time to spare. Chart the circumstances in a diary made up for the purpose.

Now, think of practical ways in which you can modify the behaviour. For example, take a deep breath and ask Bloggins if you can help him. Make a point of saying something nice at breakfast. Make sure you leave home in plenty of time to catch the bus/train.

The next part of the process of self-control involves reward. Choose something pleasant with which to reward yourself when you change the behaviour in question and reach a certain predetermined standard – buy yourself a treat if you manage to catch your bus/train every morning for a whole week without rushing!

RELAXATION

Relaxation is a useful technique to practise when you feel under stress. There are a number of similar methods, but one of the most widely used is described on pages 34–5. Read the instructions and familiarise yourself with them before having a go. You may be able to borrow a 'relaxation tape' from your general practice or local library. Do be patient, and give yourself several tries before expecting the full beneficial results – for those of us who are very 'twitchy' it can take time to learn to relax.

To begin with practise for 30 minutes three or four times a day, then slowly reduce the 'dose' to once a day as you feel better. If you feel under stress again, increase the dose!

Short routine

When you have become familiar with this technique, if you want to relax at any time when you have only a few minutes, do the sequence in shortened form, leaving out some muscle groups, but always working from your feet upwards.

For example, you might do numbers 1, 4, 6, 8 and 10 if you do not have time for the whole sequence.

PREPARING FOR RELAXATION

- Sit in a comfortable chair or (even better) lie down somewhere comfortable in a quiet, warm room where you will not be interrupted.
- If you are sitting, take off your shoes, uncross your legs and rest your arms on the arms of the chair.
- If you are lying down, lie on your back with your arms at your side. If necessary use a comfortable pillow for your head.
- Close your eyes and be aware of your body. Notice how you are breathing and where the muscular tensions are. Make sure you are comfortable.

BREATHING TO RELAX

Drop your jaw and shoulders. Start to breathe slowly and deeply, in through your nose and out through your mouth, expanding your abdomen as you breathe in, then raising your rib cage to let more air in, until your lungs are filled right to the top. Hold your breath for three to six seconds and then breathe out slowly, allowing your rib cage and stomach to relax, and empty your lungs completely.

- Do not strain – with practice it will become much easier.
- Keep this slow, deep, rhythmic breathing going throughout your relaxation session.

Remember to breathe deeply and be aware when you relax of the feeling of physical well-being and heaviness spreading through your body.

RELAXING

After five to ten minutes, when you have established a breathing pattern, start the following sequence, tensing each part of the body as you breathe in, holding your breath for ten seconds while you keep your muscles tense, then relaxing and breathing out slowly at the same time. (Note that counting ten seconds, you should say 'one hundred and one', 'one hundred and two', etc.)

RELAXATION SEQUENCE

1 Curl your toes hard and press your feet down.

2 Press your heels down and bend your feet up.

3 Tense your calf muscles.

4 Tense your thigh muscles, straightening your knees and making your legs stiff.

5 Make your buttocks tight.

6 Tense your stomach as if to receive a punch.

7 Bend your elbows and tense the muscles of your arms.

8 Hunch your shoulders and press your head back into the cushion or pillow.

9 Clench your jaws, frown and screw up your eyes really tight.

10 Tense all your muscles together.

11 After ten seconds, relax.

12 Close your eyes.

13 After you have done the whole sequence (1–11) and, while still breathing slowly and deeply, imagine a white rose on a black background. Try to 'see' the rose as clearly as possible, concentrating your attention on it for 30 seconds. Do not hold your breath during this time; continue to breathe as you have been doing.

14 Repeat step 13, visualising another peaceful object of your own choice.

15 Lastly give yourself the instruction that, when you open your eyes, you will be perfectly relaxed and alert.

16 Open your eyes.

Regular relaxation

- Improves sleep
- Increases mental and physical performance
- Combats tiredness
- Decreases anxiety and tension
- Is not addictive.

PUTTING IT ALL TOGETHER

Bring together the stress management techniques for day-to-day use through combining the monitoring of physical and mental signs of stress, use of self-instruction, deep breathing and relaxation as a means of rapid stress control.

For example, stick a red dot at the centre of your watch as a regular reminder to practise monitoring physical tension and any thoughts that might be causing stress during the day. Practise challenging thoughts (tell yourself 'stop getting worked up') or, at a minimum, ease yourself into relaxing by saying 'relax' and do this by taking a slow, deep breath, holding it for three to six seconds and letting it out slowly while practising your relaxation technique at the same time.

KEY POINTS

✓ We can defend against stress by understanding what causes it

✓ The principal defences against stress are physical and mental fitness

✓ Physical fitness is improved by healthy lifestyle, adequate sleep, eating a balanced diet and taking regular exercise

✓ Our mental fitness to deal with stress is helped by self-instruction and self-control

✓ Relaxation techniques are useful when you feel under stress

How to help yourself

Many people find their own ways of tackling stress without the help of doctors or other health professionals.

The main questions to ask yourself are:

- 'Is there anything I can do when I feel stressed that makes me feel better?' If so, keep doing it (alcohol and 'false friends' excepted).
- 'Is there anything I do that makes me feel worse?' In general, avoid it if you can.
- 'Is there anything that I think might help if only I could do it?' Try it out if at all possible.

TACKLING PROBLEMS

In addition to looking after yourself, a problem-solving approach can help you to find exactly what the stress is and devise a plan to cope with it. Even though some stresses cannot be fully resolved in this way, you will usually find that you're more able to cope, so that the overall impact of stress is reduced.

Miserable feelings and unpleasant thoughts tend to focus your attention on things you do not like about yourself or your life. They tend to exaggerate problems so that they seem overwhelming and make you feel worse. Although it may be difficult to distract yourself from unpleasant thoughts it does help to decide not to think about them and fill your mind with something else. You can do this by a combination of:

- Concentrating on events around you such as other conversations, the number of blue things you can see, in fact anything that holds your attention.
- Any absorbing mental activity you enjoy, such as mental arithmetic, games and puzzles, crosswords, reading.
- Any physical activity that keeps you occupied, such as going for a walk, doing housework or taking a trip.

Unpleasant thoughts make you tend to underestimate your positive characteristics and ability to solve problems. A number of strategies may help you achieve a more balanced view of things. Recruit a friend or relative to help you see things more clearly.

- Make a list of your three best attributes, perhaps with the help of a friend or relative. Perhaps people would describe you, for example, as generous, affectionate and reliable.
- Carry the list with you and read it to yourself three times whenever you find yourself thinking unpleasant thoughts.

- Keep a daily diary of all the small pleasant events that happen and talk about them with a friend each day.

- Recall pleasant occasions in the past and plan pleasant ones for the future, again with a friend if possible.
- Avoid talking about your unpleasant feelings – expressing unreasonable thoughts about yourself is unhelpful; tackling your real problems is more constructive.
- Ask friends to interrupt such conversations politely and focus instead on more positive ideas.
- Always consider alternative explanations for unpleasant events or thoughts rather than automatically blaming yourself.
- Keep your mind occupied by planning and doing constructive tasks – avoid sitting or lying around daydreaming or doing nothing.

Stress is almost always accompanied by symptoms of anxiety tension, worry or nervousness, such as muscle tension, trembling, cold sweats, butterflies in the stomach, rapid or difficult shallow breathing, and a rapid or irregular pounding heartbeat. This response may be triggered off by situations such as an enclosed space, a crowded supermarket, or even meeting a friend.

At other times unpleasant thoughts, for example, of dying or possible failure in work, may trigger off these feelings of anxiety and panic.

Why the panic?

It's almost always possible to identify situations or thoughts that trigger off this panicky feeling. Remember that anxiety is not harmful and always goes away after a time.

- Wait and the feelings will pass.
- Practise one of the plans below. Use it whenever you feel panicky.

- It can be helpful to start by taking a deep breath and then slowing down and deepening your breathing pattern.
- Try to distract yourself by concentrating on something pleasant as this will stop you adding to the panic.
- As the panicky feeling subsides plan something pleasant to do next.

Putting worry behind you

Worry is a pretty pointless activity and never solved anything, so here are three plans to counter it

1. Problem solving

Put your worrying to constructive use. Rather than endlessly pin-pointing your problems, pick out one or two that seem really important and make specific plans to resolve them (you may find it helpful to do this with a friend). Sit down with a sheet of paper and pencil and go through the following steps making notes as you go:

- Write down exactly what the problem is.
- List five or six possible solutions to the problem – write down any ideas that occur to you, not merely 'good' ideas.
- Weigh up the good and bad points of each idea in turn.
- Choose the solution that best fits your needs.

Plan exactly the steps you would take to achieve the solution.

- Reassess your efforts after attempting to carry out your plan (remember to praise all your efforts).
- If you are *unsuccessful* start again – this time trying a new plan.

2. Rethinking an unpleasant experience

List every feature of the experience, 'I'm sweating . . . the hairs on my arm are standing on end . . . my heart is pounding hard . . . I think I'm going to start screaming . . . my legs feel like jelly . . . I'm going to pass out'. Write these down on a card.

- Talk yourself into staying with these unpleasant feelings. Tell yourself exactly how you feel and remind yourself that the feelings will reach a peak and then get better.
- Re-label your experiences: imagine you are playing an energetic sport – a cup final,

singles finals at Wimbledon – and that this accounts for your pounding heart, rapid breathing and feelings of excitement.

- Think catastrophic thoughts, focusing your mind on the worst possible thing that could happen to you, for example, collapsing, screaming, throwing your clothes off, being sick or incontinent, etc. Plan exactly what you would do if it did actually happen. Next time it will be a little easier to cope with the feelings and with practice and monitoring you will find that you are beginning to control and overcome worry.

3. Relaxation (see pages 33–6)

Take an interest . . .

- Set some goals for your daily activities: for example, I will get up by 9 a.m., meet a friend, read an article in the newspaper.
- In *small steps*, build a full programme of constructive activities for the day.
- Avoid comparing your current levels of performance and interests with those in the past – concentrate on the here and now and on the future.
- *If a task* seems too difficult do not despair. Break it down into even easier steps and start again more slowly.
- Above all reward yourself for your efforts.
- Try to have others around you to encourage and praise you for every small step you take.

Loss of appetite

- Eat small portions of food that you particularly like.
- Take your time eating.
- Temporarily avoid situations that make you feel under pressure to finish eating.
- Drink plenty of fluids, especially water and fruit juices.
- Weight loss may be an important indicator of the extent of stress so if you continue to lose weight seek help from your GP.

Loss of sexual drive

Decreased interest in sex is frequently a feature of stress and is a cause of much distress.

It won't last forever, but in the meantime, try to enjoy those aspects of your sexual relationship that are still a pleasure. You can explain to your partner that your loss of interest and affection is a temporary symptom of your condition not a rejection of him or her.

If your interest shows no sign of reviving within a few weeks, discuss the problems with your GP and other professional adviser or confidant. Things can improve with help.

SETBACKS

Everyone has setbacks from day to day. These are to be expected and you should try to keep your mind on your long-term goals.

- Try to approach the problem in a different way.
- Try to approach the difficulty in smaller steps or stages.
- Try to continue practising because eventually this will help you overcome your difficulties.
- Remember that you will probably be more successful if you can make your activities or rewards as enjoyable as possible.

KEEP A STRESS DIARY

✓ Write down what happened

✓ Score yourself from 0 to 10 (best) for each day or week

✓ Write down all your successes, large or small

✓ Write down what self-help technique you were using, what target you were trying to achieve and whether you were practising it regularly

✓ Write down what you did not avoid thinking about or doing

✓ Write down what you did for enjoyment or fun

✓ Look back at your diary every week to see what progress you have made and to make plans for what you intend to achieve next week

It is common to think that you are not making any progress to begin with and to underrate your achievements. It's a good idea to have a member of the family or a friend to give you an independent opinion about your progress and to offer encouragement.

A simple daily or weekly record or diary will help you keep track of improvement. The first signs are usually quite small, sometimes hardly noticeable, but writing everything down will help you see exactly what has happened. Don't just rely on your memory: people have a tendency to remember setbacks more than successes. Again it is helpful to involve someone else in assessing your improvement to give an independent opinion.

KEY POINTS

✓ Many people find their own ways of tackling stress

✓ Anxiety always goes away after a time

✓ Worry is a pointless activity and never solved anything

✓ Confront your problems and make plans to solve them

✓ Everybody has setbacks – and they can be overcome

Getting help

Coping with stress can be made easier by having some support and help from family and friends. In fact, not having any family or friends to call on may itself create or worsen stress.

For example, If you are feeling anxious or uncertain about something that has recently happened, such as getting into debt or worrying that you might be going to lose your job, your stress may be increased by not having anyone to whom you can tell your fears. You may easily believe that other people don't worry in the same way, that there is no way you can escape from the pressure and that no one else is interested. You could be convinced that no one else understands or has experienced similar anxieties about such a common event, and that the fact that you are having difficulty in coping is a sign of weakness and something to be ashamed of and hidden.

Good friends and loving relationships help to counteract stress. Support can be found simply in having a stable home life or a trouble-free atmosphere at work. Such a refuge can provide breathing space, enabling us to work our way through and sort out a particularly stressful problem for ourselves.

It is an enormous help if you have someone to talk to who will listen sympathetically and in confidence and who will, if you want, provide moral support, practical advice, company or simply be there to take your mind off your problems.

Talking to someone helps you to see a problem more clearly, to get things in proportion, to explore all the possible answers and to face up to, and learn to get through, the causes of your stress.

NO ONE TO TALK TO

Many people, unfortunately, do not (or think that they do not) have any close family or good friends to turn to for help. Loneliness and isolation may be difficult to escape from; fear of rejection may put you off trying to make new friends. But the important thing is to recognise the need for outside help, and not to see this as a failure and something of which to be ashamed. If you

already have a large family and/or a social network of friends, then you will need to learn how to benefit from them in coping with stress.

If, on the other hand, feelings of isolation are a major part of the problem, you could try to develop a social network by offering friendship and support to others and receiving it from them in return. You will benefit from making the effort to find new friends and stimulation through, for example, classes, courses, sports, voluntary work or political activities.

None of these steps is easy, and all involve making a conscious effort to look outward, to be open and receptive to others, and optimistic and resilient in the face of difficulties, but they can, in time, be extremely beneficial and rewarding. Try not to forget that there are other people feeling just as isolated and with just as much potential for giving, as yourself: to find them you must come out of yourself.

WHO CAN HELP?

If you are not coping with stress, get help as soon as possible – the earlier help starts the better. You may find that the very act of seeking help and discussing problems with your family and friends gives immediate relief.

Ministers of religion

For many stressed people there is a natural tendency to turn to religion for spiritual solace and support. For those who believe, the strength of shared belief and the sense of belonging and common purpose can overcome adversity and demoralisation. Ministers of religion usually have great experience in counselling and are often more than willing to talk things over and provide support.

Voluntary bodies

Voluntary bodies such as The Samaritans can provide a sympathetic ear, information and advice. Your local health authorities have a health information service and contact numbers for local voluntary groups. Where relationship problems are important, it may be useful to contact your local branch of Relate. See 'Useful addresses' on pages 75–8.

Mental health services within the NHS

For most people the first professional contact is their GP. Often access to specialist help from psychiatrists, clinical psychologists, psychotherapists and others in the NHS can be obtained only through your GP. Occasionally specialists will agree to see you without a GP referral, but they usually want to keep your GP aware of their involvement. If you want to see a specialist but for some reason cannot get a referral, it is worth getting in touch with your local hospital to find out if you can be seen by self-referral.

Mental health services, like others within the NHS, are under severe pressure. Most people are treated by their GP and if they are referred to a hospital specialist it can take some time before they are seen.

Private specialists

You can see a psychiatrist or other mental health specialist privately. This can be arranged by your GP or by getting in touch with a local private psychiatric hospital or clinic.

Self-referral

Because of pressure on hospital services and criticism of the traditional medical approach, there are an increasing number of voluntary and private self-referral agencies. Details are usually available from your local community health council, Citizens Advice Bureau, social services department, library or community centre.

If, as well as loneliness and isolation, some more serious or specific difficulty is involved, then the various caring agencies can also provide support on a temporary or long-term basis. There are, in addition, a number of national organisations that offer help, advice and information about particular conditions or problems, and they will usually be able to give you further details about local facilities.

Notice boards in local libraries are often a good source of information about local helping agencies and facilities. Your library should have access to a copy of the Mental Health Foundation's 'Someone to Talk To' directory or a similar guide, which lists all these groups.

The essential thing is to try to identify the source of stress in your life, decide what kind of help you think would be best for you and seek help from the people or agencies that you feel most comfortable about approaching.

Also, try to recognise that, like you, the people you turn to will have different strengths and weaknesses, and if you feel that a particular approach is not working, say so, and see if it can be changed or (preferably by mutual agreement) try elsewhere.

Do not be deterred if your first approach does not bring an instant solution – keep trying.

Professional help

There are three main types of professional help available: medical, psychological and social. In practice these elements are often combined in the various treatment packages offered by different professionals – except that prescriptions for medication can be written only by medical doctors. GPs, social workers, clinical psychologists, community psychiatric nurses, counsellors and psychiatrists have important roles to play. The personal qualities of such people are important and should include acceptance, warmth, genuineness, empathy, a tolerant attitude, dependability, continuity and an interest that allows them to take even seemingly minor problems seriously.

The traditional medical approach to treatment has been criticised for being too narrow and neglecting personal and social aspects. Because of this criticism a variety of psychological approaches has been developed for use in addition to medical treatment or alone.

Your GP

For many people under stress, particularly those with no or few confidants, the family doctor becomes the first and the chief source of help. Doctors deal with all aspects of life that affect health but, like other people, they vary in their reaction to the stress responses they have to help with.

Most GPs prefer to deal with stress by counselling and general advice. Even the act of giving a full account of the circumstances surrounding the stress, with the doctor listening carefully to the descriptions, is usually beneficial because it helps to get the stress in perspective, so that adjustments and decisions can be made.

The doctor may perform a thorough examination and, in a few cases, arrange for special blood tests. The signs of stress may seem overwhelming to you and appear to mean disease, and it is reassuring to find out that no serious disease is present and that the body is functioning perfectly efficiently, even under stress.

Whatever the outcome, an appointment with the GP is a good opportunity to discuss alternative ways of reducing stress as well as where help and further information can be obtained.

SUPPORT AND COUNSELLING

GPs and most health professionals often find themselves in the position of giving emotional support, advice and counselling in an effort to provide reassurance, encouragement and sympathy.

Indeed this is probably the most common and most successful help. In many cases, listening may be more important than giving advice – provided that listening means not only hearing the words spoken but also taking note of what the person is saying and trying to understand how she or he feels.

- Your counsellor should allow you to express appropriate emotions and reassure you that they are perfectly 'normal'; a hand on the shoulder may do more good than any number of words.
- Any irrational anger and guilt you feel are accepted and not discounted.
- You can talk through events leading up to a crisis.
- You can test the reality of events described.
- You can explore the implications.
- You may find encouragement to seek new directions in life.

But beware of seeing problems as entirely due to stress and beware of becoming dependent on professional helpers.

What is counselling?

Counselling is the name given to a range of activities in which an attempt is made to understand the effects of some event on an individual or family, and to plan, with the person or people concerned, how to manage the emotional and practical realities. The purpose is not to impose an answer, but to assist the person to live the life he or she has consciously chosen.

As almost anyone can set themselves up as a counsellor, it is wise to ensure beforehand that the person you choose is trained, qualified and experienced. You can do this by asking for advice from your doctor or one of the self-help agencies.

Also, a list of qualified counsellors can be obtained by sending a self-addressed envelope to the British Association for Counselling (see page 75).

There are many different counselling techniques, but the main characteristics of a successful counsellor are emotional warmth, understanding and genuineness. You also need to feel that he or she is someone you can relate to. Counselling usually takes place regularly over a period of weeks or a few months.

Reassurance

This is still probably the most widely used form of counselling. Bland reassurance is seldom, if ever, useful, but careful listening will help identify the main stress, and then reassurance can consist of 'new' information that is relevant to reducing the stress, put in a form that is easy to understand and remember.

Behavioural counselling

Behavioural counselling aims to change behaviour. The main concern is to relieve a specific difficulty or symptom by studying the patterns of behaviour that led to difficulty, and then modifying responses by learning more useful ways of dealing with problems. The emphasis is on 'doing' rather than just 'talking'.

People who have difficulties with relationships (for example, shyness or embarrassment) can learn useful new 'social skills' in this way. After discussing and observing your behaviour, the counsellor or therapist may first explain the effects of this on other people, perhaps using a videotape to show you how you function.

When you have together identified the problems in your approach, the therapist may then coach you in new, more effective ways of behaving, and get you to act them out in a 'role play' with other people. Alternatively, the therapist may ask you to take on the role of someone with whom you have particular difficulties, to help you to see more clearly and from a different angle how your own responses work.

Rational–emotive counselling

Rational–emotive counselling considers the way in which we 'worry about being worried'. It involves identifying the irrational ways in which we think about problems, and then helps us find less stress-provoking ways of dealing with them.

Rogerian counselling

This is not based on telling us what to do, but on helping us work out for ourselves what we want and how best to achieve it. The counsellor's job is to facilitate self-understanding by 'mirroring-back' to us our own understanding, to help us to re-shape our thoughts and feelings, to share our experiences and to discuss their development with us.

Humanistic counselling

This is concerned with 'personal growth', and helping us to achieve our full potential. Workers in this form of counselling make use of encounter groups and personal therapy, massage, meditation, dancing, co-counselling and virtually any method that seems likely to help people under stress to understand themselves more clearly and to feel better. The main aim of this technique is to integrate the health and well-being of the person as a whole.

Psychotherapy

Any treatment that does not use drugs or other physical methods could be called psychotherapy. The most important element is talking and it is the ideas behind the therapy, the way it is applied and the nature of the relationships that develop between the person and the therapist which differentiate the various types of psychotherapy.

Some schools of therapy emphasise the importance of loss (of loved ones, objects or cherished ideas); others propose that we humans have an inborn tendency to seek attachments with others that build emotional and social bonds and lead to experiences of warmth, nurture and protection. Destruction of these bonds may make people vulnerable to stress.

The concept of attachment bonds provides a basis for understanding development of personality and for developing strategies to correct distortions produced by faulty or inadequate attachments in childhood.

Strong attachment bonds seem to be especially important and valuable when people are faced with adversity and stress.

Depending on the approach taken by the psychotherapist you may be helped to express and redirect anger and hostility in more appropriate ways, or you may work together to examine current personal relationships, and to understand how they have developed from experiences with attachment figures in childhood, adolescence and adulthood.

Looking at relationships

The psychotherapeutic approach to treatment has arisen out of various theories which view disturbances in personal relationships as contributing to stress and depression. Particularly important are relationship difficulties such as:

- loss or bereavement
- disputes about roles (specially the roles of husband and wife)
- role transitions (becoming a mother, divorce)
- lack of close, confiding relationships.

In essence, psychotherapeutic treatment is concerned with identifying problems in your closest relationships and in considering alternative ways of behaving and thinking.

The discussion between the person and the therapist concentrates on:

- emotions generated by close relationships (including warmth, anger, trust, envy, jealousy)
- family relationships
- friendship patterns
- work
- attitudes to neighbourhood and community.

Are there disadvantages?

Many people assume that one or other variety of psychotherapy would suit them. Psychotherapy, especially psychoanalysis, which may last years, is often prolonged, intensive and expensive. In addition it is not easily available throughout the country. It is very difficult to judge its benefits, whether it's given individually or in groups. For these reasons, and because it is possible for some people to feel worse and more stressed after psychotherapy, this treatment is generally considered inappropriate for most people.

PROBLEM-SOLVING

Problem-solving helps to:

- Define the problem
- Divide it into manageable parts
- Provide alternative solutions
- Select the best solution
- Carry it out and examine the result.

CHANGING YOUR THINKING

Your therapist may help you choose actions that are likely to change unhelpful ways of thinking – 'learning from experience'. It is not enough simply to help you change the content of a particular thought; it is essential that you should recognise and change the reasoning process that led you to a false conclusion, if you are to avoid making similar errors in the future.

Although the 'cognitive'

therapist pays particular attention to the intrusive unhelpful thoughts that precede the change of mood or feeling of stress, he or she is also concerned to question the deeper assumptions someone makes about the world, because deeper assumptions give power to unhelpful intrusive thought patterns.

The first task is to help you become aware of any unhelpful thinking and to recognise the relationship between it and emotional states. This can be done by helping you to recognise unhelpful thoughts during treatment when the stressful episode can be relived using role play.

The second task is to help you to develop different ways of interpreting events. For example, you may be encouraged to stand back from a problem in order to get a more objective view of it. Different ideas may be sought and you may be asked to rate their correctness. Once you are able to think of alternative ways of interpreting events you may be asked to keep a daily record of stressful feelings and the thoughts associated with them. You may be asked to reason with your intrusive unhelpful thoughts and suggest other possible interpretations to yourself as soon as a stressful feeling becomes apparent.

The third phase of the process is to encourage you to test out the beliefs and attitudes associated with stressful feelings in a systematic way. Instead of treating ideas as fact, you will be helped to see that it is possible to discover the degree of truth or otherwise of your beliefs through enquiry.

As you improve and learn the cognitive approach, the focus of treatment moves to deeper assumptions which are thought to underlie unhelpful thinking patterns. Unless these are identified and modified you are likely to become stressed again in the future. As these beliefs have usually been present from an early age, they tend to be resistant to change. There are no simple ways of highlighting these faulty assumptions, but a useful start is for you to identify recurring stress themes in your life. The best way to break the pattern is to encourage you to act against these deep assumptions.

Approximately 15 sessions over three months are needed for most people requiring this specialist treatment. Two sessions a week are usually held in the first month followed by weekly meetings thereafter.

SOCIAL APPROACHES

These cover all efforts to improve a patient's well-being by changing aspects of his or her social life, particularly in regard to family relationships, work and leisure activities. Of course, defined in this way virtually all treatment consists of some social elements – even visiting the GP is a social event.

At the most simple level, having

a holiday, taking time off work and taking up a new interest are all important social means of trying to relieve stress. Education, sport, music, art, nature, science and religion all offer great opportunities for social encounters that can improve well-being.

Family therapy

More complicated forms of treatment also contain a strong social ingredient. Family approaches to treatment, sometimes called family therapy, treat the person in relation to their family. This does not mean that the family is held responsible for the individual's stress, but it is clear that many of the problems of stress revolve around difficulties in the way family members communicate and relate to each other. Bringing the family together for group discussions is sometimes a powerful way of helping everyone 'pull together instead of apart', of improving communication and of helping parents develop better relationships with their children and vice versa.

Group therapy

Through discussing problems in a group over a period of a few weeks or months, this type of therapy helps combat social isolation, reminding people with stress that they are not alone, and provides the opportunity for mutual encourage-

ment and discussion of practical ways of overcoming stress.

Art therapy, play therapy, dance therapy, movement therapy, drama therapy, music therapy and gymnastics can all help people develop new social skills as well as practise old ones, increasing self-confidence and self-sufficiency. All aim to provide enjoyment, diversion, stimulation and increased self-esteem and achievement in a social context.

WHICH TREATMENT IS BEST?

The best treatment is the one that works for you. All methods have been found helpful by some people and, if one does not seem to be working after a fair trial, you should try another until you find some relief from your stress. The variety of psychological and social therapies can be quite confusing so I have listed the main ones.

TYPES OF THERAPY AVAILABLE

Supportive psychotherapy
- Aims to provide regular reassurance and encouragement.
- Sessions are informal and take place less frequently than formal psychotherapy – perhaps once a month.

Counselling
- Aims to help you help yourself by understanding why you feel the way you do and planning how to cope with emotional and practical realities.
- Helps you to live the life you have chosen by discussing current problems and alternative practical solutions.
- Provides a considerable amount of social support over several weeks or months.

Psychotherapy
- Talking is the main tool of treatment, and the different schools encourage talking about different aspects of your condition.
- Sessions usually take place weekly over a period of six to nine months.

Behavioural therapy
- Believes that behaviour is 'learned' and can therefore be 'unlearned' or changed
- Aims to stop you behaving in unhelpful or unwanted ways and to learn new patterns of behaviour that will make your life more enjoyable.
- Concentrates on how you behave at present and not on theories about why you learned to behave in certain ways. Usually lasts several months.

Cognitive therapy (also known as cognitive–behavioural therapy)
- Based on the theory that changes in our emotions and behaviour are determined by our thoughts about events that occur. If we always take a gloomy or frightened view of life, we will interpret everything that happens in a negative way.
- Aims to help you recognise and change unhelpful and gloomy ways of thinking.
- Incorporates some parts of behaviour therapy. The average course is 12–20 sessions.

TYPES OF THERAPY AVAILABLE

Family therapy
- Views you as a member of a family or similar social group.
- Is concerned with how the members of the family or group communicate with each other and with their relationships.
- Aims to resolve distress and conflict without apportioning blame by using various psychotherapeutic methods over a period of months.

Group therapy
- This comprises a group of people, who did not know each other before, coming together with a therapist to help each other with their problems.
- Groups may be made up of people with the same problem or different problems, and they may be single sex or mixed.
- Group members can see that they are not alone in having problems and can get a great deal of support from other members of the group. Usually lasts some months.

Psychoanalysis
- Believes that our behaviour and mental state originate in early experiences in childhood.
- Different schools of psychoanalysis interpret the meaning of what you say differently.
- A great deal of time is spent discussing the relationship between you and the therapist – this is taken to represent the relationship between you and important people in your early life such as your mother or father.
- Psychotherapy sessions take place several times a week over a period of years and so the treatment can be costly in terms of both time and money.

SELF-HELP GROUPS

These are groups of people who have a common problem and have joined together to do something about it. They are small, voluntary groups providing mutual aid working together towards the accomplishment of some aim, and provide members with the following help:

- People with stressful problems can feel lonely, confused and isolated, and it can help to talk about these problems with others 'in the same boat'.
- Support may be given individually or in a group. It may be aimed at helping the individual to adjust to a situation or to take steps to change it. It may be offered in crises or may be available over a longer term.
- Self-help groups provide a wealth of information to help people cope more easily.
- Some forms of help needed to cope with particular problems can be provided directly by mutual aid organisations. These may be provided on a casual or informal basis (for example, baby-sitting), or they may be provided more formally (established playgroups). They may be carried out by group members on a voluntary basis or they may involve hired staff. A few groups even provide services jointly with their local authority.

- Many self-help groups consider that the benefits and services provided by the State are inadequate and so they form a pressure group to bring about favourable changes.

THE MEDIA

Newspapers, books, magazines, television, radio and the internet aim to entertain, inform and instruct. Although they are usually passive forms of communication, when used selectively they may be useful in providing practical information about a wide range of interests, and give temporary relief from stress by diverting attention from worries.

THE TELEPHONE/INTERNET

The telephone/Internet gives confidential access to an enormous number of counselling organisations nation- and worldwide. The most notable source of confidential telephone contact is The Samaritans. Its 24-hour telephone service is provided in the main by part-time volunteers of all ages and from all walks of life, who have training but whose main strength lies in their willingness to listen sympathetically.

TIME – THE GREAT HEALER

Perhaps the most neglected treatment of all is time. Mild stress can get better on its own, given time, and spontaneous improvement over 6 to 12 weeks is the norm. Quite a lot of people do get better anyway, sometimes in spite of the treatment prescribed! Spontaneous natural improvement is most likely, however:

- in a first episode of stress
- when the stress started recently
- where the stress started suddenly
- when relatives and friends can give practical and emotional support.

KEY POINTS

✓ Family and friends can provide valuable support in dealing with stress

✓ If you are worried about stress, the earlier you tackle it and help begins the better

✓ There are three main types of professional help available: medical, psychological and social

✓ Give a treatment a fair chance to help you before trying something else

✓ Self-help groups and the media can provide a wealth of information, advice and practical help

Smoking tobacco, drinking excess alcohol and taking drugs of dependence (sometimes even sleeping tablets, benzodiazepines or tranquillisers prescribed by the doctor, if not carefully monitored) make stress worse; they are habits that are unwise and should be stopped or severely curtailed. They are false friends because they provide the illusion of temporary relief, making the processes of defence and successful adaptation much more difficult.

People under stress sometimes attempt to cope, either deliberately or unconsciously, by using these substances to deal with the symptoms they are experiencing or to withstand the pressure that they feel under.

ALCOHOL

Alcohol in moderation may be a pleasure, but it is a potentially addictive drug with many subtle and complicated effects. Any long-standing stressful situation invites the serious risk of heavy drinking and eventual dependence on alcohol, which can wreck marriages, family and social life, careers and health (and, of course, you should

A UNIT OF ALCOHOL IS

A small glass of sherry or fortified wine

A standard glass of wine

$^1/_2$ pint of beer or cider
$^1/_4$ pint of strong lager

A single measure of aperitif or spirit

A bottle of spirits – brandy, whisky or gin – contains about 30 units

never drive after drinking).

A 'unit' of alcohol may be defined as the equivalent of half a pint of beer or cider (of normal strength), a single measure of sherry, Martini, etc., a single measure of spirits or a small glass of wine. The average man or woman will react to units of alcohol as shown in the tipple table on page 61, with women affected at lower 'doses' than men, the effects being increased by factors such as lack of food, tiredness and stress – and rapid consumption.

Dependence on alcohol

The increasing signs that you may be developing a dependence on alcohol are:

- Awareness of a compulsion to drink.
- Developing a daily drinking pattern.
- Drinking takes priority over other activities.
- Your tolerance for alcohol changes – this usually increases at first but eventually falls.
- Repeated symptoms of alcohol withdrawal – nausea, headache, nervousness, shaking, sweating, tenseness, jitteriness, being 'on edge'.
- Relief or avoidance of withdrawal symptoms by further drinking.
- Rapid return of the features of dependence after a period of abstinence.

Not all these signs may be present, and any one may occur to variable degrees in different people.

'Safe drinking'

Safe levels of drinking are difficult to define precisely for each person, and depend on factors such as sex, body size and constitution. The levels are lower for women than for men.

What is a sensible limit? A unit of alcohol is as described earlier, and medical advice is that the limit for men should be no more than 21 units a week and, for women, up to 14 units a week (if pregnant, alchohol should probably be avoided). In both cases, the units should be spread throughout the week, with two or three drink-free days.

How much is too much? For men, 36 units or more in a week, and for women 22 units or more in a week. It is worth remembering that, on average, it takes one hour for the body to get rid of the alcohol in one unit.

TIPPLE TABLE

Number of small glasses of wine	Effects
Units 1–2	Feeling good and relaxed, but reaction time noticeably reduced
2–4	Some loss of inhibition with poor judgement. Accidents become more likely
3–5	Noticeable loss of inhibition, with physical clumsiness. Beyond the legal limit for driving
4–7	Loss of physical control. Obviously drunk with extreme reactions. Above this level there is progressive loss of consciousness by degrees

Note: women are affected at lower doses than men. The orange glasses denote the numbers of glasses for women, the orange + red for men.

TIPS TO HELP CUT DOWN DRINKING

Reduce the overall amount by stopping drinking at certain times, for example, lunch time, and do something else instead.

- Keep busy, plan activities that will keep your mind off drink.

- Avoid reminders of drinking and, whenever possible, places where alcohol will be consumed or people who offer you a drink.

- Plan avoidance action for times when you are confronted by these particular situations.

- Drink a long soft drink to quench your thirst before starting on alcohol.

- Allow yourself only one alcoholic drink an hour at any drinking session.

- Add mixers to wines and spirits to increase the volume and so help slow down consumption.

- Avoid drinking in 'rounds' if you are likely to break the above rules.

Remember that what others choose to drink is irrelevant to your health. Try to find some non-alcoholic alternative in drinking situations.

A man who drinks eight or more units a day (56 a week), or a woman who drinks more than five units a day (35 a week) is at great risk of developing an alcohol-related problem.

You may find it useful to involve a supportive relative or friend who can put up a united resistance with you.

SMOKING

The most common reason that cigarette smokers give for not stopping smoking is stress, but cutting out (or certainly cutting down) smoking should be the number one health priority. Tell a smoker that his habit is killing him, however, and the first thing he will probably decide to do is light a cigarette!

The most important step in giving up is the decision that you really do want to stop.

Once you make that decision you are halfway there and, if you feel you need some help, it may be worth considering some form of nicotine replacement therapy (NRT): anything from nicotine gum to nicotine patches, the latter being worn on the skin for either 12- or 24-hour periods (depending on which kind you opt for).

Both work by allowing the body to adjust gradually to lower amounts of nicotine. The gum is available on prescription, although the patches can be bought from the chemist – the pharmacist will be able to advise you on the type of NRT that is most appropriate for you.

However, it's worth remembering that all these replacements are aids, not cures.

Unfortunately, the reasons for stopping smoking actually make it harder to stop. First, because they create a feeling of sacrifice (being

QUIT SMOKING

Initially, forget the 'sensible' reasons for stopping and ask yourself:

- What is smoking doing for me?

- Do I actually enjoy it?

- Do I really need to go through life spending a fortune just to stick these things in my mouth and make myself ill?

forced to give up a little friend, prop, pleasure or however the smoker views cigarettes) and, second, because they create a bind – we do not smoke for the reasons we should stop – which prevents us from asking ourselves the real reasons for wanting or needing to smoke.

Remember that you had no need to smoke before you became hooked. The first cigarette probably tasted awful, and you had to work quite hard to become addicted. The most annoying part is that non-smokers do not seem to be missing out on anything; in fact, smokers keep smoking to achieve the same state of 'tranquillity' as non-smokers.

So why do you smoke? Forget about stress, boredom and all the other reasons you may think you have; there are two real reasons – nicotine addiction and brain-washing.

Nicotine addiction

Nicotine is one of the fastest-acting addictive drugs known to human-kind. The concentration in the bloodstream falls quickly, however, to about half, in some 30 minutes after finishing a cigarette and to only a quarter within an hour.

The withdrawal pangs from nicotine are so subtle that most smokers do not even realise that they are drug addicts. Fortunately, it is a relatively easy drug to 'kick' once you have accepted that this is the case. There is no physical pain, just an empty, restless feeling, the feeling of something missing. If withdrawal is prolonged, the smoker becomes nervous, insecure, agitated, lacking in confidence and irritable. Within seconds of lighting a cigarette, nicotine is supplied, resulting in the feeling of relaxation and confidence that the cigarette gives. As soon as this cigarette is put out, the chain starts again. The

SIX STEPS TO GIVING UP SMOKING

1 You decide that you really want to do it, and realise that you can achieve your goal. Remember that smokers are not weak-willed and that it is only indecision that makes giving up more difficult.

2 Recognise and think about the fact that you are addicted to nicotine, but remember that withdrawal is not as painful as you think it is going to be, and that it takes only about three weeks to rid the body of 99% of the nicotine.

3 Look forward to the freedom. Do not be afraid of losing the prop you have been brainwashed into believing you need. Smoking enslaves you, preventing you from achieving the peace and confidence you used to have as a non-smoker.

4 Stop smoking completely. Remember there is no such thing as just one cigarette – smoking is a drug addiction and a chain reaction. By moping about the one cigarette, you will be punishing yourself needlessly.

5 Watch out for smokers – they may feel threatened by the fact that you have given up, and may try to tempt you back.

6 Keep reminding yourself that there is nothing to give up. On the contrary, there are enormous positive gains to be made by not smoking.

difficulty is that it is when you are not smoking that you suffer the feelings, and you do not, therefore, blame the cigarette. When you light up you get relief and are fooled into believing that the cigarette is the cure for the bad feelings.

So we smoke to feed the little monster, but we decide when to do it and we do it more in stressful situations, when we need to concentrate, when we are bored and when we wish to relax.

Brainwashing
Nicotine addiction is not the only problem and it is relatively easy to cope with (the smoker does not, for instance, wake up through the night craving a cigarette).

Another major difficulty is 'brainwashing'. The unconscious is a very powerful element in our minds and, despite a whole host of anti-smoking campaigns, we are still bombarded with extremely clever advertising which tells us that cigarettes relax us and give us confidence, and that the most precious thing on earth is a cigarette. Once addicted to nicotine, the power of the advertising is increased, which simply enforces the fear of giving up.

KEY POINTS

✓ Smoking, drinking alcohol and taking drugs of dependence are not a cure for stress – they all make stress, and coping with stress, worse

✓ While drinking alcohol in moderation can be a pleasure, heavy drinking carries serious risks to health and well-being – personal, family and at work

✓ Stress is the most common reason smokers give for not stopping smoking

✓ Nicotine is one of the fastest-acting addictive drugs known

✓ Smoking not only ruins your health, it also ruins your finances

Pills, potions and complementary methods

We are experiencing an increasing national dependence on drugs, pills and painkillers of all kinds. We are in danger of reaching the point where we believe that every ache, pain or worry must be soothed away by taking some kind of treatment, encouraging the idea that any form of stress is harmful. There is a strong link between an overtly pill-conscious society and one that includes a growing number of people dependent on drugs. Some varieties of sleeping tablets and tranquillisers show this connection by the pleasurable effects they induce in vulnerable people. Experiencing these effects may lead to dependence, and can bring all the complications of dependence on stronger drugs, including withdrawal symptoms if they are stopped, and a desperate need to have a good supply in case they are needed.

Many people find complementary therapies of benefit. These include yoga, meditation, autogenic training, biofeedback, the Alexander technique, acupuncture and aromatherapy. Some of these are available at little or no cost, others may prove more expensive.

COMPLEMENTARY THERAPIES

Acupuncture
This is an ancient Chinese medical technique for relieving pain, curing disease and improving general health, and consists of inserting needles into any of hundreds of points located over various 'meridians'. It is a treatment that aims to alter the flow of an individual's bodily energy or life force to relieve pain and restore health.

Alexander technique
This technique teaches people new ways of thinking and using their bodies, with a view to eliminating the effects of unconscious bad habits, such as tension and contorted posture, thereby improving physical and psychological well-being. It is a way of life rather than a therapy.

Aromatherapy
Pure essential oils (obtained from aromatic plants by steam distillation) are used to soothe tension and improve health and mental well-being. The oils are usually massaged into the body, but may also be inhaled, blended or used in baths. Essential oils can temporarily alter our moods and release stress.

Autogenic training
This method of self-hypnosis emphasises individual control over bodily processes through specific exercises. Training usually takes between two and three months, and you learn standard training exercises aimed at inducing a feeling of well-being and coping ability. Specific exercises deal with, for example, breathing, blood flow and skin temperature. Profound muscular relaxation is achievable.

Biofeedback
Information supplied instantaneously about your bodily processes, for example, blood pressure or heart rate, is monitored electronically and 'fed back' to you by a gauge on a meter, a light or a sound. You learn to detect physical reactions and establish control over them. It can help alleviate symptoms such as pain and muscle tension, and its effects can be lasting if used in combination with counselling to help the person understand reactions to stress.

Meditation
This consists of a number of techniques of concentration and contemplation, which can be effective in controlling pulse and respiratory rates, and in the control of migraine and high blood pressure. Transcendental meditation has been reported to help through reduction of tension, lowering anxiety, and increasing job satisfaction and work performance. Meditators spend two daily 20-minute sessions in a quiet comfortable place, silently repeating their mantra.

Yoga
This is a useful technique for physical and mental relaxation and consists of exercises in physical posture to condition the body. Mastery is reckoned by the ability to hold the postures for an extended period without involuntary movement or physical distractions. Instruction emphasising both the physical and spiritual benefits of yoga techniques is widely available.

PERSONAL DEFENCE MECHANISMS

Adapting to stress is a two-stage process. First, we have to realise that some of our repeated responses to continuing stress may be unhelpful; second, we need to explore and use new ways of coping until satisfactory solutions are found.

You may sometimes hear social workers, counsellors and psychologists using words such as 'denial' and 'rationalisation' to describe the way people respond to stress. These are technical terms which most people do not come across in everyday speech. I explain them briefly over the next page or so.

Some of these repeated, unhelpful responses – defence mechanisms – are described below. Remember, though, that these are only ideas that may help us understand ourselves by showing how our minds work and how we react to stress.

* **Compensation** – developing a behaviour to offset a defect or sense of inferiority, e.g. running a pet sanctuary to make up for inadequate human relationships. Thus over-compensation occurs when compensation is overdone.

* **Conversion** – hidden fears may be 'converted' and come to the surface in the form of bodily symptoms. Someone who is afraid of going out may develop a weakness in the legs.

* **Denial** – persuading oneself that there is nothing really wrong when, in fact, there is. This is done in the hope that the trouble will somehow go away – for example, refusing to admit that you are ill.

* **Displacement** – shifting an emotion from one target to another. Ideas or attitudes which make us uncomfortable may be disguised or avoided in this way. For example, anger with our workmates may be taken out on our family.

SHIPS?... I SEE NO SHIPS!

✓ Get your priorities right – sort out what really matters in your life.

✓ Think ahead and try to anticipate how to get ro difficulties.

✓ Share your worries with family or friends whenever possible.

✓ Try to develop a social network or circle of friends.

✓ Exercise regularly.

✓ Lead a regular lifestyle.

✓ Give yourself treats and rewards for positive actions, attitudes and thoughts.

✓ Get to know yourself better – improve your defences and strengthen your weak points.

✓ Think realistically about problems and decide to take some appropriate action; if necessary, distract yourself in a pleasant way – don't 'bottl things up' or sit all night brooding.

✓ Try to keep things in proportion.

✓ Don't be too hard on yourself.

✓ Seek medical help if you are worried about your health.

✓ There are always people who are willing and able to help, whatever the problem – don't be unwilling to benefit from their experience.

✓ Relax and take short rests throughout the day, every day.

✓ Make small, regular changes to your lifestyle.

✓ Learn to delegate.

✓ Make space for leisure time.

✓ Have proper breaks for meals.

✓ Make time for yourself every day and every week.

✓ Listen carefully to those around you.

✓ Enjoy yourself, and your family and friends.

- **Dissociation** – avoiding looking too closely at our attitudes so that inconsistencies in our thoughts and conduct are overlooked.

- **Fixation** – 'fixed' personal behaviour which is more appropriate to earlier, less mature periods. This is seen in grown adults who depend, child-like, on others.

- **Identification** – conscious or unconscious modelling of oneself on another person, which may include the assumption of his or her dress, leisure activities, etc. This may be quite normal: for example, young people often imitate the attitudes and behaviour of older people whom they hold in high regard.

- **Introjection** – the turning inwards on oneself of the feelings and attitudes towards others, which gives rise to conflict and aggression. Unspoken anger with other family members may then lead to self-harm.

- **Inversion** – the exaggeration of tendencies opposite to those that are repressed (see below). Prudery, for example, may be an inversion of repressed sexual desire.

- **Projection** – the opposite of introjection, the displacement of personal attitudes on to others or the environment. This is another way of avoiding self-blame and guilt. Personal inadequacies are blamed on others or even on the environment.

- **Rationalisation** – a form of self-deception in which socially acceptable reasons are found for conduct that is prompted by less worthy motives.

- **Regression** – going back to the ways of thinking, feeling and behaving which are more appropriate to earlier stages of individual or social development. Thus, an adult may regress to childish temper tantrums.

- **Repression** – the pushing out of consciousness of ideas and impulses that do not fit in with what the individual regards as correct in the circumstances. Repression is unconscious and involuntary, in contrast to suppression, which is the intentional refusal to have thoughts or feelings, or carry out actions that conflict with moral standards.

- **Resistance** – a barrier between the unconscious and conscious mind, preventing the resolution of tensions or conflicts. For example, someone might unconsciously resist enquiring into the origins of his stress, thereby prolonging his condition.

- **Sublimation** – the direction of undesirable or forbidden tendencies into more socially acceptable channels. For example, childish, self-indulgent behaviour is sublimated into entertaining or altruistic social behaviour in the process of maturity. Surplus energy may be sublimated into useful channels.

• **Transference** – the experience of emotions towards one person which are derived from experience with another. For example, anxious or hostile feelings previously felt towards a domineering parent may, in later life, be felt in relation to figures of authority.

• **Withdrawal** – giving up, and physical and emotional retirement from a stressful situation, characterised by loss of enthusiasm and interest, apathy and daydreaming

USING THE GOLDEN RULES

If you stick to the Golden Rules, on pages 70–1, you will help yourself become calmer and more relaxed. You will have to keep working at it to get the full benefit; work out a practical routine and stick to it, not just for a few days. And remember to enjoy yourself – that is the best cure for stress. Learn to relax and take things easy for at least an hour each day – a warm bath, taking your time, enjoying pleasant feelings, a relaxing walk or reading an interesting book can help release you from the things that cause you stress.

Breathe deeply and gently, count to ten, and think again. Take one day at a time – accept a bad day, tomorrow may be better.

KEY POINTS

✓ Becoming dependent on pills and potions creates further problems

✓ Many people find alternative therapies such as yoga of benefit

✓ Overcome stress by understanding and controlling your response to it

✓ Remember to use the golden rules for reducing stress

Conclusion

Although we cannot, and indeed must not, avoid stress, we can learn to meet it efficiently and live with it successfully, rather than letting stress overwhelm us to the extent that it affects both our mental and physical health.

Because of the enormous individual differences in the causes of stress, and in our abilities to cope, this book cannot hope to give all the answers to everyone's problems. What I have tried to do, however, is to help you think about, and identify, the undesirable stresses in your own life, and learn how to control these – either alone or with the help of others.

Taking stock of ourselves and our lives from time to time can be an extremely beneficial exercise. It is amazing how little we question our priorities and how many sources of unnecessary stress we can get rid of by doing this.

Useful addresses

Accept Services UK
(alcohol-related problems)
724 Fulham Road
London SW6 5SE
Helpline: 020 7371 1777
Fax: 020 7384 3967
Email: accept@accept-
services.demon.co.uk

Age Concern England
Freepost (SWB 30375)
Ashburton, Devon TQ13 7ZZ
Tel: 0800 009966 (7 days, 7am–7pm)
Fax: 020 8765 7211
Email: infodcp@ace.org.uk
Website: www.ace.org.uk

Age Concern Scotland
113 Rose Street
Edinburgh EH2 3DT
Tel: 0131 220 3345
Fax: 0131 220 7779
Email: enquiries@acscot.org.uk
Website:
www.ageconcernscotland.org.uk

Age Concern Northern Ireland
3 Lower Crescent
Belfast B7 1NR
Tel: 028 9024 5729
Fax: 028 9023 5497
Email: info@ageconcernni.org

Age Concern Cymru
4th Floor, 1 Cathedral Road
Cardiff CF11 9SD
Tel: 029 2037 1566
Fax: 029 2039 9562
Email: enquiries@accymru.org.uk
Website: www.accymru.org.uk

Alcoholics Anonymous
General Service Office
PO Box 1, Stonebow House
Stonebow, York YO1 7NJ
Helpline: 0845 769 7555
Tel: 01904 644026
Fax: 01904 629091
Website: www.alcoholics-
anonymous.org.uk
Northern Ireland
Tel: 028 9043 4848

Check your local phone directory or
newspaper for local meetings.

Alzheimer's Disease Society
Gordon House
10 Greencoat Place
London SW1P 1PH
Helpline: 0845 300 0336 (Mon–Fri
8.30am–6.30pm)
Tel: 020 7306 0606
Email: info@alzheimers.org.uk
Website: www.alzheimers.org.uk

**ASH (Action on Smoking and
Health)**
102–108 Clifton Street
London EC2A 4HW
Tel: 020 7739 5902
Fax: 020 7613 0531
Email:
action.smoking.health@dial.pipex.com
Website: www.ash.org.uk

See also Quit below.

Association for Post-Natal Illness

145 Dawes Road, Fulham
London SW6 7EB
Tel: 020 7386 0868
Fax: 020 7386 8885
Email: info@apni.org
Website: www.apni.org

British Association for Counselling and Psychotherapy (BACP)

1 Regent Place
Rugby CV21 2PJ
Tel: 0870 4435252
Fax: 0870 4435160
Minicom: 01788 572838
Email: bac@bac.co.uk
Website: www.counselling.co.uk

Brook Advisory Service

Studio 421, Highgate Studios
53–79 Highgate Road
London NW5 1TL
Helpline: 0800 0185023 (Mon–Fri 9am–5pm)
24-hour information line: 020 7617 8000
Fax: 020 7284 6050
Email: admin@brookcentres.org.uk
Website: www.brook.org.uk

Service for under-25s. Advice on all aspects of sexual health. Has 17 local offices.

Carers UK

20–25 Glasshouse Yard
London EC1A 4JT
Helpline: 0808 808 7777(Mon–Fri; 10–12 a.m., 2–4 p.m.)
Tel: 020 7 490 8818
Fax: 020 7490 8824
Email: info@ukcarers.org
Website: www.carersuk.demon.co.uk

ChildLine

(for children requiring counselling)
Freepost 1111, London N1 0BR
ChildLine: 0800 1111
Admin enquiries:
Royal Mail Building, Studd Street
London N1 0QW
Tel: 020 7239 1000 (admin enquiries only)

Fax: 020 7239 1001
Website: www.childline.org.uk

Compassionate Friends

53 North Street, Bristol BS3 1EN
Helpline: 0117 953 9639
(7 days, 10.00am–4pm; 6–10.30pm)
Fax: 0117 914 4368
Email: info@tcf.org.uk
Website: www.tcf.org.uk

Offers help and support for bereaved parents and their families.

Cruse Bereavement Care

Cruse House, 126 Sheen Road
Richmond, Surrey TW9 1UR
Helpline: 0870 167 1677 (Mon–Fri 9.30am–5pm)
Tel: 020 8939 9530
Fax: 020 8940 7638
Email: info@crusebereavementcare.org.uk
Website: www.crusebereavementcare.org.uk

Depression Alliance

35 Westminster Bridge Road
London SE1 7JB
Tel: 020 7633 0557
Fax: 0207 633 0559
Email: information@depressionalliance.org
Website: www.depressionalliance.com

Eating Disorders Association

1st Floor, Wensum House
103 Prince of Wales Road
Norwich NR1 1DW
Helpline: 0845 634 1414
(8.30am–8.30pm Mon–Fri)
Youth helpline: 0845 634 7650
(4–6.30pm Mon–Fri)
Fax: 01603 664915
Email: info@edauk.com
Email (under 18s): talkback@edauk.com
Website: www.edauk.com

Family Planning Association

2–12 Pentonville Road
London N1 9FP
Tel: 020 7837 5432
Fax: 020 7837 3042
Contraceptive helpline: 0845 310 1334
(Mon–Fri 9am–7pm)
Website: www.fpa.org.uk

Fellowship of Depressives Anonymous
Box FDA, c/o Self Help Nottingham
Ormiston House
32–36 Pelham Street
Nottingham NG1 2EG
Tel: 01702 433838
Fax: 01702 433843
Email: fdainfo@aol.com

Self-help group for people who suffer from depression and their carers. There are local groups in England.

Gamblers Anonymous
PO Box 88
London SW10 0EU
Helpline: 0870 50 88 80 (24 hours)
Information: 01426 947800
Website:
www.gamblersanonymous.org.uk

Self-help group for compulsive gamblers. *See also* GamAnon and GamCare.

GamAnon
Email:
gamanon@gamblersanonymous.org.uk
Website: www.gamanon.org.uk

Provides support and encourage ment for the families and friends of compulsive gamblers.

GamCare
Helpline: 0845 6000133 (24 hours)
Website: www.gamcare.org.uk

For young people addicted to gambling.

Help the Aged
207–221 Pentonville Road
London N1 9UZ
Seniorline (welfare rights): 0808 800 6565 (Mon–Fri 9am–4pm)
Tel: 020 7278 1114
Fax: 020 7278 1116
Email: info@helptheaged.org.uk
Website: www.helptheaged.org.uk

Manic Depression Fellowship
Castle Works
21 St George's Road
London SE1 6ES
Tel: 020 7793 2600
Fax: 020 7793 2639
Email: mdf@mdf.org.uk
Website: www.mdf.org.uk

MIND
(National Association for Mental Health)
Granta House, 15–19 Broadway
Stratford, London E15 4BQ
Information line: 0845 7660 163
(Mon–Fri 9.15am–5.15pm)
Tel: 020 8519 2122
Fax: 020 8522 1725
Email: contact@mind.org.uk
Website: www.mind.org.uk

Miscarriage Association
c/o Clayton Hospital
Northgate, Wakefield
Yorkshire WF1 3JS
Tel: 01924 200799 Mon–Fri 9am–4pm)
Fax: 01924 298834
Email:
miscarriageassociation@care4free.net
Website:
www.miscarriageassociation.org.uk

NHS Direct Telephone Service
UK except Scotland (*see* NHS24): 0845 4647
Textphone: 0845 606 4647

Nurse advice and health information service 24 hours a day.

NHS Direct Online
England and N Ireland:
www.nhsdirect.nhs.uk
Wales: www.nhsdirect.wales.nhs.uk

NHS24 (Scotland)
Tel: 0800 224488 (9am–8pm)
Website: www.nhs24.com

National Association of Bereavement Services
20 Norton Folgate, Liverpool Street
London E1 6DB
Referral line: 020 7247 1080
(Mon–Fri 7am–12pm)
Fax: 020 7247 0617

A national coordinating body for bereavement services, promoting networking, training and professional standards.

National Family Mediation
Star House, 104–108 Grafton Road
London NW6 4BD
Tel: 020 7485 8809
Fax: 020 7284 1881
Email: general@nfm.org.uk
Website: www.nfm.u-net.com

National Phobic Society
339 Stretford Road
Manchester M15 4ZY
Tel: 0161 227 9898
Fax: 0161 227 9862
Email: natphob.soc@good.co.uk
Website: www.phobics-society.org.uk

Nexus
(an association of unattached people – not a helpline)
6 The Quay, Bideford EX39 2HW
Helpline: 0800 834221 (Mon–Fri 9am–6pm)
Fax: 01237 425142
Email: info@nexus-uk.co.uk
Website: www.nexus-uk.co.uk

Parentline Plus
520 Highgate Studios
53–79 Highgate Road
Kentish Town
London NW5 1TL
Tel: 020 7284 5500
Helpline: 0808 800 2222 (24h)
Textline: 0800 7836 783
Fax: 020 7284 5501
Email:
centraloffice@parentlineplus.org.uk
Website: www.parentlineplus.org.uk

Provides support and information to parents and carers, chiefly through a confidential and anonymous telephone helpline.

Quit
211 Old Street
London EC1V 9NR
Tel: 020 7251 1551
Fax: 020 7251 1661

Email: reception@quit.org.uk
Website: www.quit.org.uk

QuitLines
(for help in stopping smoking)
NHS helpline: 0800 1690169 (Mon–Fri 9am–11pm)
Northern Ireland: 02890 663281 (Mon–Fri 9am–5pm)
Scotland: 0800 848484 (Mon–Sun 12am–12pm)
Wales: 08457 697500 (24 hours)
See also Quit

Relate
National Office:
Herbert Gray College
Little Church Street
Rugby CV21 3AP
Tel: 01788 573241
Fax: 01788 535007
Email: enquiries@national.relate.org.uk
Website: www.relate.org.uk

Provides counselling for people with emotional, sexual or other problems in their relationships with partners. There are over 120 branches throughout the UK.

Release
(Drug-related problems)
388 Old Street, London EC1V 9LT
Tel: 020 7729 9904 (Mon–Fri 10am–6pm)
Out of hours: 020 7603 8654
Fax: 020 7729 2599
Email: info@release.org.uk
Website: www.release.org.uk
Drugs in Schools
(Aimed at young people and their families)
Tel: 0808 8000800 (Mon–Fri 10am–6pm)

Samaritans
The Upper Mill
Kingston Road
Ewell KT17 2AF
Berks SL1 1QP
24-hour national helpline: 08457 909090
See local phone book for nearest local helpline number

Fax: 020 8394 8301
Email: jo@samaritans.org (sender's identity known)
Website: www.samaritans.org.uk

Nearly 200 branches across the country; 24-hour service every day of the year.

Sexual Health and National AIDS Helpline
Tel: 0800 567 123
Fax: 0151 703 7775
Website: www.nat.org.uk

Free, 24-hour and confidential advice on HIV, AIDS and other sexually transmitted infections.

Stillbirth and Neonatal Death Society (SANDS)
28 Portland Place
London W1B 1LY
Helpline: 020 7436 5881 (Mon–Fri 10.30am 3.30pm)
Tel: 020 7436 7940
Fax: 020 7436 3715
Email: support@uk-sands.org
Website: www.uk-sands.org

Terence Higgins Trust
52–54 Grays Inn Road
London WC1X 8JU
Helpline: 020 7242 1010 (12 noon–10pm)
Fax: 020 7242 0121
Email: info@tht.org.uk
Website: www.tht.org.uk

Counselling, support and information for bereavement and AIDS.

Victim Support
Cranmer House, 39 Brixton Road
London SW9 6DZ
Helpline: 0845 303 0900 (Mon–Fri 9am–9pm; Sat, Sun 9am–7pm; bank hols 9am–5pm)
Fax: 020 7582 5712
Email: contact@victimsupport.org.uk
Website: www.victimsupport.org
Admin: 020 7735 9166

Westminster Pastoral Foundation
(counselling)
23 Kensington Square
London W8 5HN
Tel: 020 7361 4800
Fax: 020 7361 4808
Email: counselling@wpf.org.uk
Website: www.wpf.org.uk

Yoga Therapy Centre
90–92 Pentonville Road
Islington
London N1 9HS
Tel: 020 7689 3040
Fax: 020 7689 3048
Email: yogatherapy@virgin.net
Website: www.yogatherapy.org

Yoga therapy is a specialised adaptation of yoga to help people with health problems.

THE INTERNET AS A SOURCE OF FURTHER INFORMATION

After reading this book, you may feel that you would like further information on the subject. One source is the internet and there are a great many websites with useful information about medical disorders, related charities and support groups. Some websites, however, have unhelpful and inaccurate information. Many are sponsored by commercial organisations or raise revenue by advertising, but nevertheless aim to provide impartial and trustworthy health information. Others may be reputable but you should be aware that they may be biased in their recommendations. Remember that treatment advertised on international websites may not be available in the UK.

Unless you know the address of the specific website that you want to visit (for example, familydoctor.co.uk), you may find the following guidelines helpful when searching the internet.

There are several different sorts of websites that you can use to look for information, the main ones being search engines, directories and portals.

Search engines and directories
There are many search engines and directories that all use different algorithms (procedures for computation) to return different results when you do a search. Search engines use computer programs called spiders, which crawl the web on a daily basis to search individual pages within a site and then queue them ready for listing in their database.

Directories, however, consider a site as a whole and use the description and information that was provided with the site when it was submitted to the directory to decide whether a site matches the searcher's needs. For both there is little or no selection in terms of quality of information, although engines and directories do try to impose rules about decency and content. Popular search engines in the UK include:

google.co.uk
aol.co.uk
msn.co.uk
lycos.co.uk
hotbot.co.uk
overture.com
ask.co.uk
espotting.com
looksmart.co.uk
alltheweb.com
uk.altavista.com

The two biggest directories are:

yahoo.com
dmoz.org

Portals
Portals are doorways to the internet that provide links to useful sites, news and other services, and may also provide search engine services (such as msn.co.uk). Many portals charge for putting their clients' sites high up in your list of search results. The quality of the websites listed depends on the selection criteria used in compiling the portal, although portals focused on a specific group, such as medical information portals, may have more rigorous inclusion criteria than other searchable websites. Examples of medical portals can be found at:

nhsdirect.nhs.uk
patient.co.uk

Links to many British medical

charities will be found at the Association of Medical Research Charities (www.amrc.org.uk) and Charity Choice (www. charitychoice. co.uk).

Search phrases

Be specific when entering a search phrase. Searching for information on 'cancer' could give astrological information as well as medical: 'lung cancer' would be a better choice. Either use the engine's advanced search feature and ask for the exact phrase, or put the phrase in quotes – 'lung cancer' – as this will link the words. Adding 'uk' to your search phrase will bring up mainly British websites, so a good search would be 'lung cancer' uk (don't include uk within the quotes).

Always remember that the internet is international and unregulated. Although it holds a wealth of invaluable information, individual websites may be biased, out of date or just plain wrong. Family Doctor Publications accepts no responsibility for the content of links published in their series.

Index